How to Press
FLOWERS

Sallie K. Paris

Knoxville, Tennessee
crippledbeaglepublishing.com

Cover and book design by Jody Dyer

ISBN 978-1-970037-91-3

Published and printed in the United States of America.

In loving memory of my grandmothers,
Jeanette Cumbaa Rhodes and
Freddy Louise Houston Kirkland,
who taught me to love flowers...
and not to take life too seriously.

How to Press Flowers

As you've probably gathered, this book is a lighthearted attempt to illustrate just how simple it is to press flowers. The pages are blank for many reasons. First, flowers bleed, and if there were some spellbinding poem printed on the page, you might miss a word or two thanks to the innocent flower's pigment smears. Second, you can use these pages to journal the creative ideas that come to you as you dig in the dirt to the tunes of birdsong. Third, you may want to record your landscaping tasks or plan a bed or garden. Finally, maybe you have a crush on your handsome neighbor and need to use this book as a disguise for your diary, in which you'll record all the reasons you admire Mr. Neighbor Man.

If, though, you do indeed want to press flowers, these pages are ready. Use the left side to document dates, species, and other details. Lay the flowers on the right side to, well, press them. Close the book. The process is that easy. You can then stack weights, garden stones, other books, or other heavy objects (maybe that handsome neighbor man has some tool you need to borrow), on top of the book to finish the task.

Leave the book in a warm, dry place. Wait a few days or weeks. Be patient. The specimen is the boss and must no longer be damp. When the petals, stem, and leaves are completely dry, use your little green thumb and other fingers to carefully remove the flower. Then you may create a variety of art forms as a tribute to Mother Nature.

Notes

Sketches

Notes

Sketches

Notes

Sketches

Notes

Sketches

Notes

Sketches

Printed in Great Britain
by Amazon

9693059e-51e6-43c5-a642-5b61a6a9793cR01